THE MAGICAL UNICORN SOCIETY

OFFICIAL COLOURING BOOK

Members of the Magical Unicorn Society have studied the seven unicorn families for centuries. They have collected hundreds of images of these beautiful creatures, some of which are compiled in this book for unicorn enthusiasts and colouring fans everywhere.

The wonderful thing is unicorns come in a rainbow of colours – from sunflower yellow to sky blue, and stunning indigo to peachy pinks – so let your imagination and your coloured pens and pencils run wild.

Selwyn

101ST PRESIDENT OF THE
MAGICAL UNICORN SOCIETY

Michael O'Mara Books Limited

Est. 1577

Mountain Jewels

Mountain Jewel unicorns are known for their short
tempers and gruff personalities. These two have had
a disagreement, which has started a fiery battle.
They are fighting with their horns, which spark
like fireworks when they clash.

Mountain Jewel unicorns are wary creatures that don't often trust humans. Many years ago, special people called 'Whisperers', from the mountain city of Mandu in Central Asia, befriended a group of Mountain Jewels. As a sign of their trust, the unicorns showed the Whisperers a hidden jewel mine that was full of priceless, glittering gems.

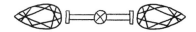

Found in some of the harshest environments on Earth, Mountain Jewel unicorns can survive high altitudes and cold temperatures. They can emit beams of light and heat from their horns and are fiercely loyal to each other.

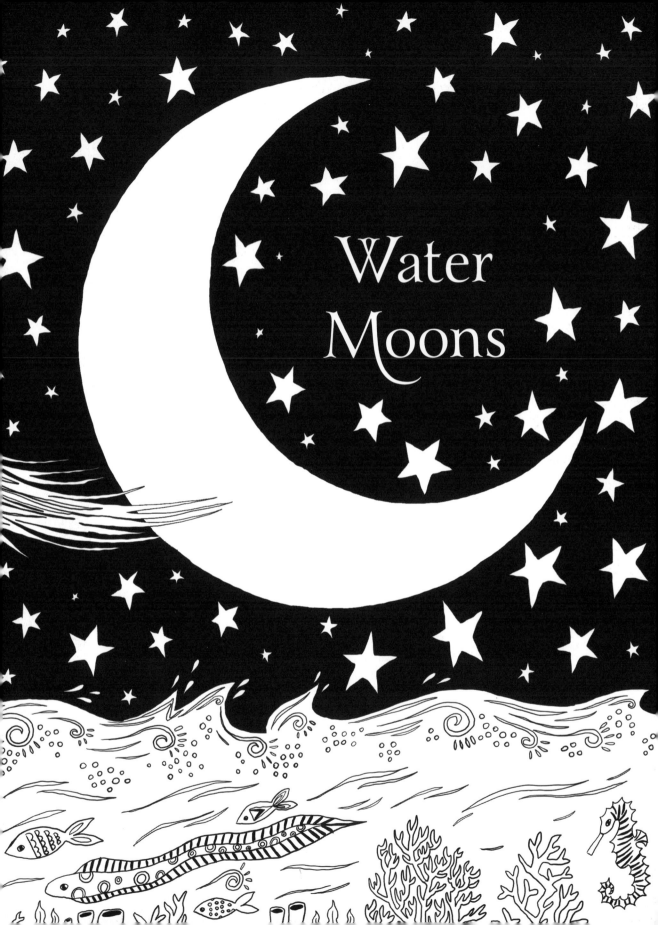

Water Moon unicorns live in and beside water.
They are found on the banks of rivers and lakes
and on the shores of oceans around the world.
This pair of Water Moons are in Egypt,
wading through the River Nile.

Legends tell of Water Moon unicorns who live far out at sea. They gallop through the waves and can survive treacherous storms. These unicorns have kind hearts and will lead sailors and their ships to safety when they sense a dangerous storm brewing.

Unless they are standing under the light of the Moon,
Water Moon unicorns are invisible to humans.
Sea creatures have stronger senses than people
and can feel when a Water Moon is nearby.

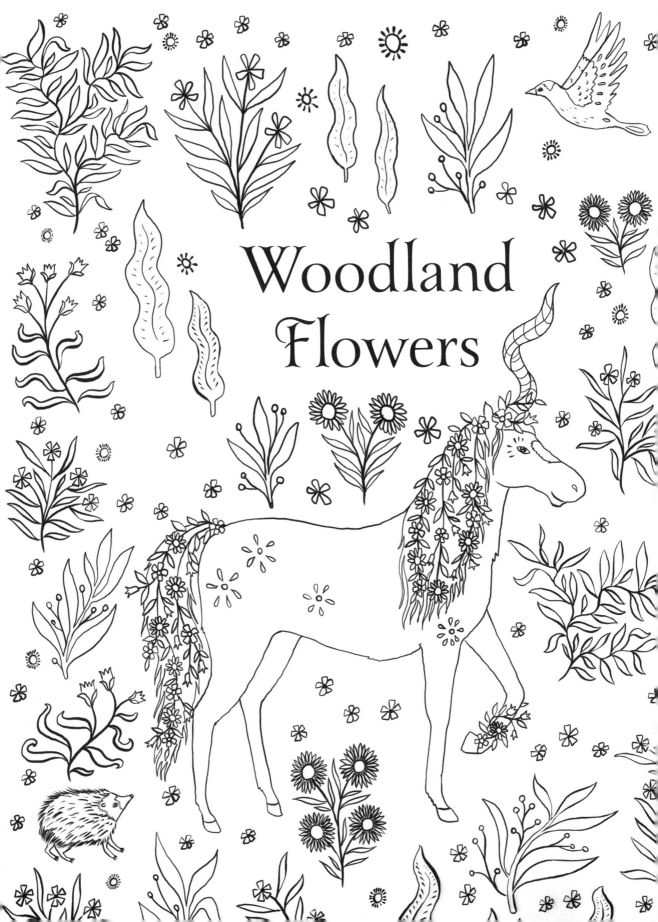

Woodland Flowers

In the French countryside, cloaked by a dense, magical forest, stands the Château de Temps, which was once home to a medieval royal family. The beautiful castle is protected by a blessing, or group, of Woodland Flower unicorns. These magical creatures make sure that no harm ever comes to the castle or the humans that live there.

Woodland Flower unicorns are gentle creatures with colourful forest flowers intertwined with their manes. They have brown, velvety coats and curled horns with an antler-like texture.

Woodland Flower unicorns live in magical forests
and have lots of animal friends. They can communicate
with other creatures using their telepathic powers.
Folklore says that if someone is in need of help,
Woodland Flowers can be summoned with song.
You can also find these unicorns by following
their distinctive heart-shaped hoof prints.

Desert
Flames

The mighty Desert Flames are the only unicorn family gifted with the power of flight. Often found living in hot desert landscapes, these hardy creatures are some of the fastest in the world, whether galloping on land or soaring through the air.

First discovered in 10th-century Persia, Desert Flame
unicorns are often featured in local murals and on
ceramic tiles. Here is an arabesque-style tile that was
found in the grand palace of a famous maharajah, or king.

Like many other desert creatures and plants, Desert Flame unicorns have adapted to the dry and desolate environments in which they live. They know just how to find a magical oasis, where there is food to eat and water to drink. Desert Flames are very caring creatures that will help other animals or humans in distress.

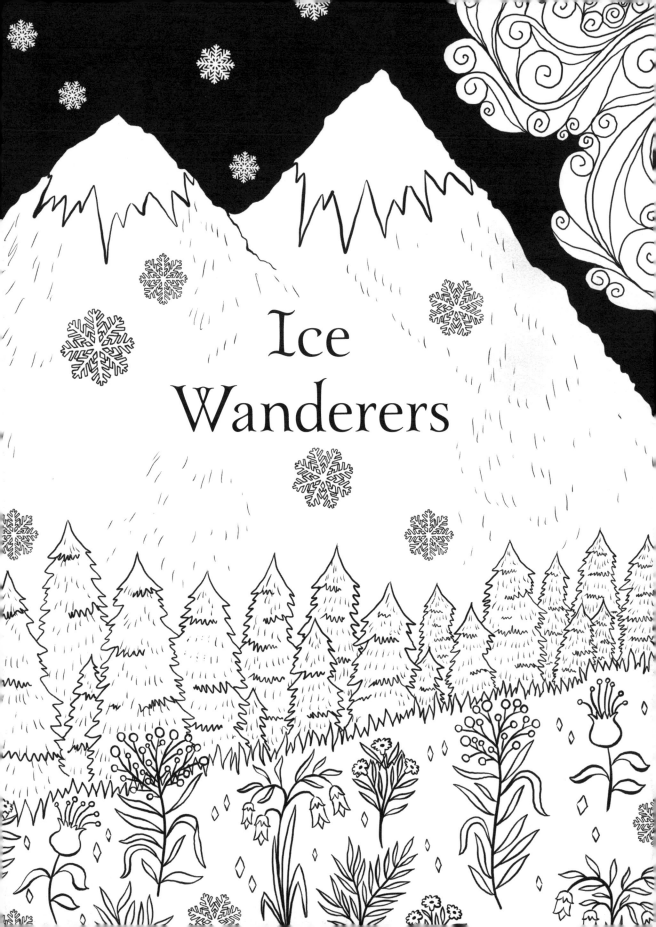

Ice Wanderers

Ice Wanderer unicorns live on the freezing glaciers near the North and South Poles. This frisky Southern Ice Wanderer loves to swim in the icy waters and frolic with the seals and penguins that live there.

Even when they are far apart, Ice Wanderer unicorns can communicate with other members of their blessing, or group. They send messages by shooting bright lights up into the sky with their horns. These beautiful light displays appear in many colours from vibrant green to warm pink. Some people call them the Northern or Southern Lights.

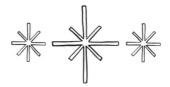

Ice Wanderer unicorns are perfectly suited to cold climates. Their thick, luscious coats keep them warm, while acting as camouflage. They can become almost invisible when they don't want to be found.

Storm
Chasers

An ancient South American legend tells of the four mischievous Storm Chaser unicorns whose job it was to hold up the sky. However, they were a cheeky bunch who loved to play, not work. They would often drop the sky and cause floods of rain and bursts of lightning to crash to the ground.

Some types of Storm Chaser unicorns have neon-yellow manes and tails that crackle with electric charge. Their horns, which are made of cloudy-grey opal, act like lightning conductors. When electric bolts flash down from the sky and strike a Storm Chaser's horn it will spark with electricity. They can use this power to protect other creatures from the deadly bolts.

Storm Chasers are the only unicorns who have complete control over the weather. They can channel lightning, change the course of a rain cloud and bring sunshine, warmth and magic to places that need it most.

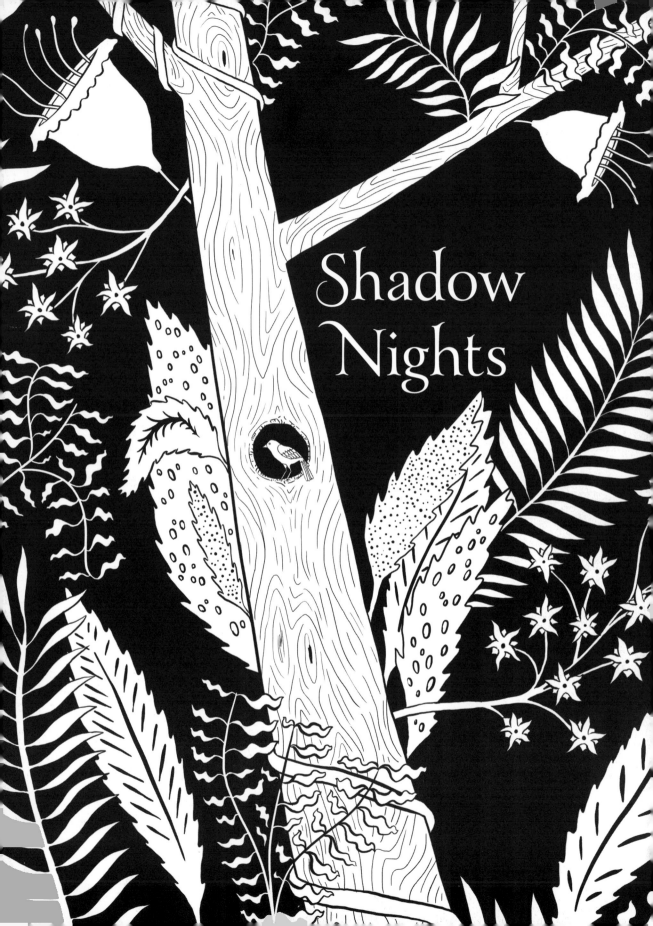

Shadow
Nights

Shadow Night unicorns can exist everywhere
and nowhere at once. They are ethereal creatures,
made of pure magic, and can move through the
spirit realm as well as the earthly world.

Shadow Night unicorns have been spotted in the jungles of South America. If you look carefully into the shadows there, you might just be lucky enough to see a glinting unicorn eye staring back at you.

If you see an unexplained shadow pass across
a mirror, it could mean a Shadow Night is near.
These unicorns have magical healing powers and
can also influence humans' dreams.

A POSTSCRIPT FROM SELWYN

You, too, can become a member of the Magical Unicorn Society. Simply log on to our website and follow the instructions.

www.magicalunicornsociety.co.uk

Written by Selwyn E. Phipps
With special thanks to Katy Lennon
Illustrated by Harry and Zanna Goldhawk,
Ciara Ni Dhuinn and Oana Befort
Edited by Katy Lennon
Designed by Zoe Bradley
Cover Illustration by Harry and Zanna Goldhawk
Cover Design by Angie Allison

First published in Great Britain in 2018 by Michael O'Mara Books
Limited, 9 Lion Yard, Tremadoc Road, London SW4 7NQ

W www.mombooks.com
F Michael O'Mara Books
Y @OMaraBooks

Text and design copyright © Michael O'Mara Books Limited 2018
Illustrations 2–3, 8–9, 16–17, 24–25, 32–33, 40–41, 48–49, 56–57
copyright © Harry and Zanna Goldhawk 2018
All other illustrations copyright © Michael O'Mara Books Limited 2018

A CIP catalogue record for this book is available from the British Library.

ISBN: 978-1-78929-056-1

2 4 6 8 10 9 7 5 3 1

Printed in Malta